The
Christopher Norton

COUNTRY PRELUDES

Collection

16 original pieces
for solo piano
based on Country styles
with playalong CD

BOOSEY & HAWKES

Boosey & Hawkes Music Publishers Ltd
www.boosey.com

Published by Boosey & Hawkes Music Publishers Ltd
Aldwych House
71–91 Aldwych
London
WC2B 4HN

www.boosey.com

This compilation © copyright 2007 by Boosey & Hawkes Music Publishers Ltd

ISMN M-060-11749-7 (979-0-060-11749-7)
ISBN 978-0-85162-515-7

First impression 2007

Printed in England by the Halstan Printing Group, Amersham, Bucks

Piano: Christopher Norton
Tracks: Frank Mizen
Produced by Christopher Norton for CN Productions
www.christophernorton.com

CONTENTS

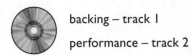
backing – track 1
performance – track 2

1. COUNTRY RAG

Christopher Norton

2. BORDER TUNE

Christopher Norton

6

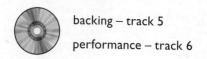

backing – track 5
performance – track 6

3. SOUTHERN FRIED

Christopher Norton

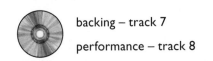

backing – track 7

performance – track 8

4. HOMECOMING

Christopher Norton

Sedately ♩ = c 76

mp

Con ped

mf cresc.

slowing to the end

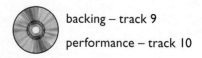
backing – track 9
performance – track 10

5. BAR-ROOM STRUT

Rollicking ♩ = c 126

Christopher Norton

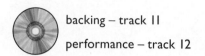

6. ROVING RIVER

Christopher Norton

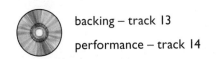

backing – track 13

performance – track 14

7. MUSTANG

Christopher Norton

Rhythmically ♩ = c 88

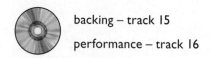

backing – track 15

performance – track 16

8. RIGHT TIME, WRONG PLACE

Christopher Norton

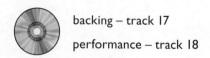

backing – track 17

performance – track 18

9. FOREST'S EDGE

Christopher Norton

Precisely ♩ = c 160

10. COUNTRY GIRL

Christopher Norton

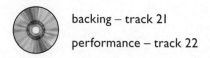

backing – track 21

performance – track 22

11. COWBOY BLUES

Christopher Norton

Slowing to the end

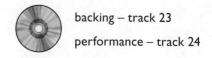

backing – track 23

performance – track 24

12. HOT ROD

Christopher Norton

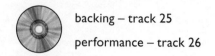

backing – track 25

performance – track 26

13. SITTING ON THE PORCH

Christopher Norton

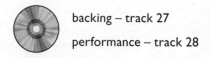

backing – track 27

performance – track 28

14. SHE DONE ME WRONG

Christopher Norton

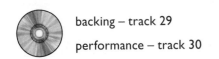

backing – track 29

performance – track 30

15. RIDING HIGH

Christopher Norton

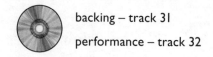
backing – track 31

performance – track 32

16. BARNSTORMING

Christopher Norton